MATHS DICTIONARY

PETER ROBSON

Newby Books

PO BOX 40, SCARBOROUGH,
NORTH YORKSHIRE, YO12 5TW
TEL/FAX 01723 362713
www.newbybooks.co.uk

ALWAYS

1) read the question carefully all the way through

2) decide which method to use

3) show all your working - as neatly as you can

4) write the answer clearly, with units (such as m, cm^3, hours, etc.) if necessary

5) check for any careless errors

ACUTE ANGLE An angle of less than 90°

ALTERNATE ANGLES Angles between parallel lines, on
    alternate sides of a transversal. Angles in a Z shape

    Alternate angles are EQUAL
    e.g.

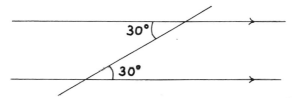

ANNULUS The space between two concentric circles

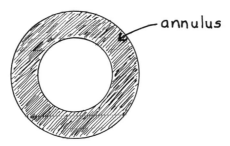

ANTICLOCKWISE The opposite way to the hands of a clock

APEX The corner opposite the base of a figure

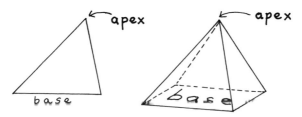

APPROXIMATION A rough answer

ARC Part of the circumference of a circle

    e.g.

AREA The space inside a plane figure. Area is measured in SQUARE units (e.g. SQUARE metres, SQUARE centimetres, etc.)

<u>Area of rectangle</u> = base x height (<u>or</u> length x breadth)

    e.g.

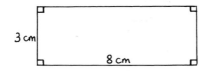

Area = 8 x 3

      = 24 cm²

<u>Area of triangle</u> = ½ base x height

    e.g.

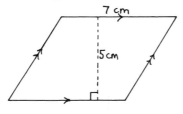

Area = ½ x 8 x 3

      = 12 m²

<u>Area of parallelogram</u> = base x height

    e.g.

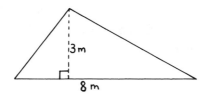

Area = 7 x 5

      = 35 cm²

<u>Area of trapezium</u> = ½ (base + top) x height

    e.g.

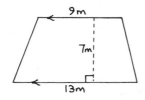

Area = ½ (13 + 9) x 7

      = 77 m²

<u>Area of circle</u> - πR^2 (<u>or</u> $\pi \times$ radius $\times$ radius)

e.g.

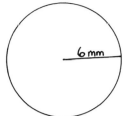

Area = 3.14 × 6 × 6
    = 113.04 mm²

AREAS OF SIMILAR FIGURES

If length is 2 times, AREA is 4 times (2 x 2)
If length is 3 times, AREA is 9 times (3 x 3)
If length is 4 times, AREA is 16 times (4 x 4)
etc.

AVERAGE Same thing as MEAN

$$\text{Average} = \frac{\text{Sum of quantities}}{\text{Number of quantities}}$$

e.g. Find the average of 62, 61, 66, 59, 68, 57 and 68
Sum of quantities = 62+61+66+59+68+57+68 = 441
Number of quantities = 7

Average $= \dfrac{441}{7} = 63$

AVERAGE SPEED

$$\text{Average speed} = \frac{\text{Total distance}}{\text{Total time}}$$

AXIS

x axis is the <u>along</u> axis
(horizontal axis)

y axis is the <u>up</u> axis
(vertical axis)

If you are talking about them both,
they are called AXES
(pronounced ax-eez)

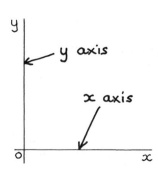

AXIS OF SYMMETRY A folding line which makes one half of a figure fit (or map) exactly on to the other half

e.g.

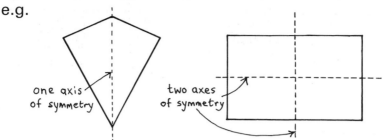

one axis of symmetry

two axes of symmetry

BAR CHART A statistical diagram made up of bars

e.g.

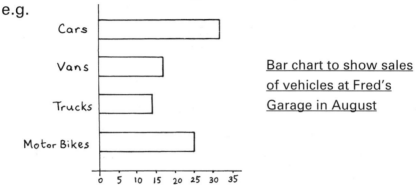

Cars

Vans

Trucks

Motor Bikes

0 5 10 15 20 25 30 35

Bar chart to show sales of vehicles at Fred's Garage in August

BASE (1)   The bottom of a figure

(2)   The counting system being used

e.g. Base 10 (DENARY) is ordinary counting, using 0,1,2,3,4,5,6,7,8 and 9

Base 4 is counting with only 0, 1, 2 and 3.
Base 2 (BINARY) is counting with only 0 and 1,   etc.

BEARING Another name for DIRECTION

(a)   Bearings are measured from NORTH
(b)   Bearings are measured CLOCKWISE
(c)   Bearings have THREE figures (Fill up with noughts if needed)

ALWAYS FIND WHERE THE BEARING IS FROM, AND ALWAYS DRAW NORTH FIRST e.g.

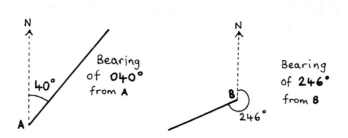

Some useful bearings

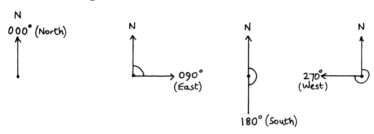

BINARY Base 2. Counting with only 0 and 1.

The kind of counting used by a computer

The first ten numbers in binary are 1, 10, 11, 100, 101, 110, 111, 1000, 1001, 1010

The first eight binary columns are

<u>128</u>   <u>64</u>   <u>32</u>   <u>16</u>   <u>8</u>   <u>4</u>   <u>2</u>   <u>1</u>

BINOMIAL An expression containing two terms

e.g. a – 2b

BISECT Cut exactly in half

BISECTOR A line which cuts another line or an angle exactly in half

A <u>perpendicular bisector</u> is a line which cuts another line exactly in half at right angles

e.g.

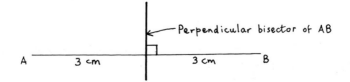

BLOCK GRAPH A statistical diagram made up of blocks

e.g.

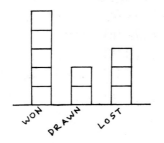

Block graph to
show results of
ten matches

CANCEL Divide the top and bottom of a fraction by the same
number to make the fraction simpler

e.g.

$$\frac{\cancel{12}^{3}}{\cancel{20}_{5}} = \frac{3}{5} \qquad \frac{\cancel{4}^{2}}{7} \times \frac{5}{\cancel{6}_{3}} = \frac{10}{21}$$

CAP Same as INTERSECTION of sets. Written ∩

CENTRE OF ROTATION The point that a figure is rotated about

CHORD A straight line joining two points on the circumference
of a circle

e.g.

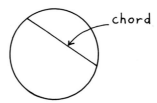

chord

CIRCUMFERENCE The perimeter of a circle. All the way round
a circle. Circumference = 2πR

e.g.

14 cm

Circumference $= 2 \times \frac{22}{7} \times 14$

$= 88$ cm

CLOCK **24-hour Clock** Way of measuring time without using a.m., p.m., morning, evening, etc.

       1.00 a.m. is called 01 00

       2.00 a.m. is called 02 00   etc.

       1.00 p.m. is called 13 00

       2.00 p.m. is called 14 00   etc.

For times AFTER 12.59 p.m., add 12 hours to the ordinary time, e.g.

      6.45 p.m. is written   6.45

$$\begin{array}{r} 6.45 \\ +12 \\ \hline 18\ 45 \end{array}$$

CLOCKWISE The same way as the hands of a clock

COEFFICIENT The figure in front of a letter

e.g.   5a   The coefficient of a is 5

         7m   The coefficient of m is 7

COLUMN GRAPH A statistical diagram made up of columns

e.g.

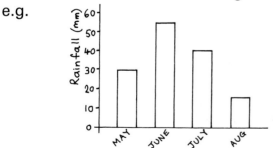

A column graph to show rainfall in the months May to August

COLUMN MATRIX A matrix with only one column

e.g.

$$\begin{pmatrix} 3 \\ 14 \\ -7 \end{pmatrix}$$

COMMON Something shared by both or all things
e.g. These two triangles have a common side AB

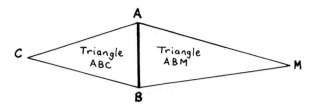

The Highest <u>Common</u> Factor (H.C.F.) of 48 and 80 is 16, because 16 is the highest factor shared by both 48 and 80

COMPLEMENTARY ANGLES Angles which add up to 90°
e.g.

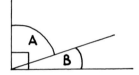

Angles A and B are complementary. Angle A is the complement of angle B, and angle B is the complement of angle A

CONCENTRIC CIRCLES Two or more circles with the same centre

CONE A circular pyramid
e.g.

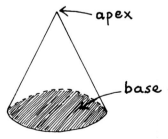

CONGRUENT Two (or more) figures - often triangles - which are identical, i.e. exactly the same shape and exactly the same size - but they need not be the same way round

e.g. These triangles are CONGRUENT

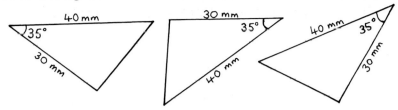

CONSECUTIVE NUMBERS Numbers which follow one another
e.g. 9, 10, 11 are consecutive numbers

CONVERSION GRAPH A line graph to convert one kind of unit
to another
e.g. Conversion graph for temperature (degrees C and
degrees F)

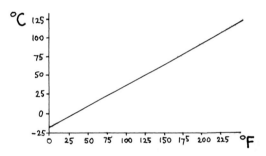

COORDINATES Mathematical map-references to show the
position of a point. The x coordinate (along) comes first;
then the y coordinate (up)

Coordinates are always written in brackets with a comma
between the two numbers
e.g.

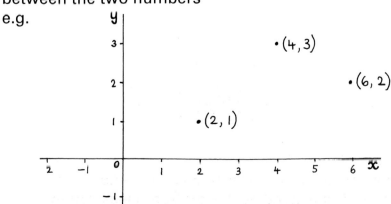

CORRESPONDING ANGLES Angles between parallel lines and a transversal, which are exact copies of one another

Corresponding angles are EQUAL

e.g.

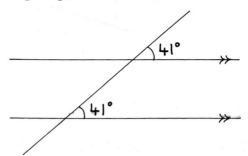

COSINE of an angle (often written **cos**)

$$\text{Cosine} = \frac{\text{Adjacent}}{\text{Hypotenuse}}$$

e.g.

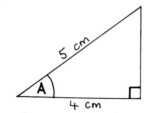

$\cos \mathbf{A} = \frac{4}{5} = \mathbf{0 \cdot 8}$

CUBE (1) A solid with 6 faces which are all squares

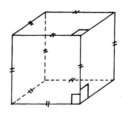

(2) A number multiplied by itself and then by itself again

e.g. The cube of 2 = 2 x 2 x 2 = 8

<u>Cubed</u> means 'multiplied by itself and then by itself again'

Cubed is written to the power 3

e.g. 5 cubed = 5^3 = 5 x 5 x 5 = 125

CUBOID A solid with 6 faces which are all rectangles. An ordinary box shape
   e.g.

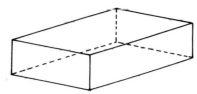

CUP Same thing as UNION of sets. Written ∪

CYCLIC QUAD A 4-sided plane figure which fits exactly into a circle
   e.g.

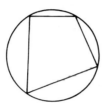

CYLINDER A circular prism
   e.g.

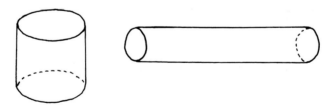

DECAGON A plane figure with 10 sides

DECIMAL PLACES The number of figures after the decimal point
   e.g.   2.34   has 2 decimal places
           0.0915 has 4 decimal places

DECREASE When you decrease something you make it smaller

DENARY Base 10. Ordinary counting 1, 2, 3, 4, 5, 6, 7, 8, 9, 10, 11, 12, etc.

DENOMINATOR The bottom number of a fraction.
The denominator tells you WHAT SORT of fraction

DETERMINANT The determinant of the matrix

$$\begin{pmatrix} A & B \\ C & D \end{pmatrix} \text{ is } (A \times D) - (C \times B)$$

e.g. The determinant of matrix $\begin{pmatrix} 1 & 3 \\ -2 & 0 \end{pmatrix}$

is $(1 \times 0) - (-2 \times 3) = 6$

DIAGONAL A straight line from one corner of a plane figure to another corner, going across the space inside
e.g.

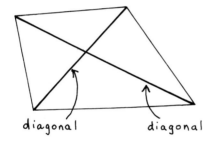

diagonal   diagonal

A pentagon has 5 diagonals

The number of diagonals in an N-sided figure
is $\frac{1}{2} N (N - 3)$

DIAMETER The distance across the middle of a circle.
A line which bisects a circle, making two semi-circles

The diameter is twice the radius

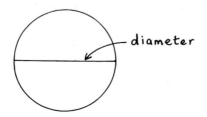

diameter

DIFFERENCE The answer to a subtraction (take away)

e.g. The difference between 17 and 43 is

$$43 - 17 = 26$$

DIGIT A single figure

e.g. 1536 has four digits (1, 5, 3 and 6)

600000 has six digits (6, 0, 0, 0, 0 and 0)

DISJOINT SETS Sets which are not connected. Sets which have no common members. Sets which have no intersection

e.g. The sets

{elephant, rhinoceros, giraffe}

and

{2, 3, 5, 7, 11, 13, 17}

are disjoint. They have no common members

DISTRIBUTION TABLE A table to show how many things there are in each group. Used for making statistical diagrams

e.g.

Distribution table to show ages of guests at the White Swan Hotel on a certain Saturday night

Age	Under 21	21-40	41-60	61-80	Over 80
Number of guests	12	15	11	4	0

DIVIDEND The number you divide INTO in a division

DIVIDING (Tests for)

A number will divide by 2 if it ends with 0, 2, 4, 6 or 8

A number will divide by 3 if its digits, added up, divide by 3

e.g. 5832 will divide by 3 because 5 + 8 + 3 + 2 = 18, and 18 will divide by 3

A number will divide by 5 if it ends with 0 or 5

A number will divide by 10 if it ends with 0

DIVISOR The number you divide BY in a division

EDGE The line joining two corners of a solid

e.g.

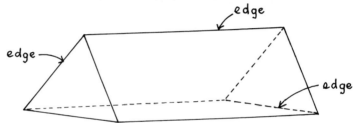

ELEMENT One of the things in a set. A member of a set of things

e.g. 4 is an ELEMENT of the set 2, 4, 6

ENLARGEMENT Transforming a figure to make a larger similar figure

e.g.

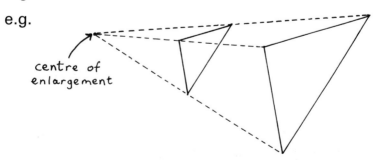

EQUATION Two (or more) things which are equal

e.g. $2a - 5 = 27$

EQUIDISTANT Both (or all) the same distance from something

e.g. P, Q, R, S and T are equidistant from A

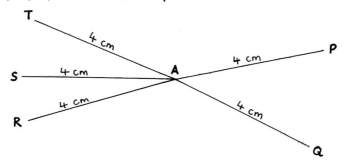

EQUILATERAL TRIANGLE A triangle with all its sides equal length and all its angles 60°

e.g.

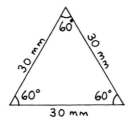

ESTIMATE The rough answer. Find the rough answer

EULER'S THEOREM for solids

Faces + Corners = Edges + 2

EVALUATE Find the value of. Find how much it comes to

EXPRESSION One or more terms expressing a quantity
e.g. The cost in pence of y loaves at 22p each,
(y− 3) cakes at 9p each and a chicken pie at 35p is given by the
expression

$$22y + 9(y - 3) + 35$$

EXTERIOR ANGLES The angles on the OUTSIDE of a polygon
Exterior angles of any polygon add up to 360°

e.g.

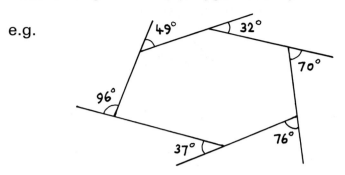

FACE The flat part of the outside of a solid
e.g. This box has six faces (a base, a top and four faces round
the sides)

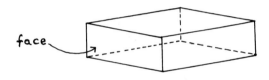

face

FACTOR A number which divides into another number
e.g. 1, 2, 3, 4, 6, 8, 12 and 24 are all FACTORS of 24 because
they all divide into 24

A <u>prime factor</u> is a prime number which divides into another
number

e.g. 2 and 3 are prime factors of 24

24 expressed as a product of its prime factors
is 2 x 2 x 2 x 3   <u>or</u> 2^3 x 3

FACTORISE Find the factors of
e.g. Factorise $2a^2 - 6ab$
                              $2a(a - 3b)$

FREQUENCY CHART Same as DISTRIBUTION TABLE

GRADIENT The slope of a graph. Gradient at any place on the graph is found by dividing y by x

e.g.

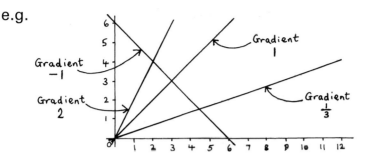

Gradient of a travel graph tells you the SPEED

H.C.F. Highest Common Factor. The highest number which will divide into two (or more) other numbers
e.g. The H.C.F. of 12, 20 and 32 is 4, because 4 is the highest number which will divide into them all. Of course, 2 is also a common factor but it is not the highest

HENCE From what you have already done

HEPTAGON A plane figure with 7 sides

HEXAGON A plane figure with 6 sides

HISTOGRAM A statistical diagram, like a column graph with no gaps, for showing continuous (gradual) information
e.g.

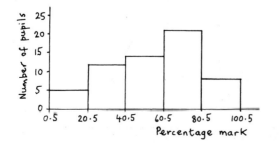

Histogram to show percentage exam marks of 60 pupils at St. Gregory's School

HORIZONTAL Straight across. Parallel to the horizon. At right angles to vertical

HYPOTENUSE The longest side of a right-angled triangle (the side opposite the right angle)

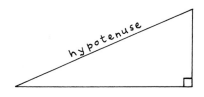

IMAGE The result of a transformation. The figure which appears when you translate, reflect, rotate or enlarge something

IMPROPER FRACTION A fraction with the top number bigger than the bottom

e.g. $\dfrac{8}{5}$ $\dfrac{25}{7}$

If an answer comes out as an improper fraction it should be changed to a mixed number, e.g.

$$\frac{14}{5} = 2\frac{4}{5}$$

INCREASE When you increase something you make it larger

INDEX The power of a number

e.g. 4 is the index (or power) in 3^4
3 is the index (or power) in 5^3

When there are several of them they are called INDICES (pronounced indi-seez)

INEQUALITY Two (or more) things which are not equal

e.g. $5N - 2 < 17$

The common signs for inequality are
- $<$ is less than
- $>$ is more than (<u>or</u> greater than)
- $\leqslant$ is less than or equal to
- $\geqslant$ is more than or equal to (is at least)

INTEGER (pronounced <u>in</u>-ti-jer) A whole number
Positive integers are + whole numbers, e.g. 1, 18, 453
Negative integers are – whole numbers, e.g. –5, –42, –3500

INTEREST The extra amount added to money which is being borrowed or lent. Often written as a percentage

e.g. I save (or lend to a savings company) £100 at 9% per year interest. At the end of one year I shall have £100 + interest of £9 which makes a total of £109

INTERIOR ANGLES The angles on the INSIDE of a polygon.
Interior angles of an N-sided polygon add up to
$180(N-2)$ degrees

e.g.

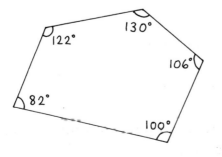

Interior angles
of a pentagon
(5-sided figure)
add up to
180 (5 –2)
= 540°

INTERSECTION (1) The point where two or more lines meet

e.g.

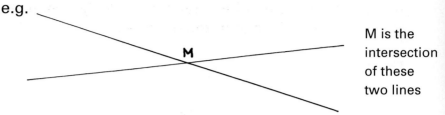

M is the intersection of these two lines

(2) A set of things which are in both (or all) sets at the same time. Intersection is written ∩

e.g. If set A   =   {3, 6, 9, 12, 15}
     and set B =   {2, 4, 6, 12}

the INTERSECTION of sets A and B
     A ∩ B = {6, 12}
because 6 and 12 are in both sets A and B at the same time

INVERSE MATRIX The inverse of the matrix

$$\begin{pmatrix} A & B \\ C & D \end{pmatrix} \text{ is } \frac{1}{d}\begin{pmatrix} D & -B \\ -C & A \end{pmatrix}$$

where d is the determinant (AD − BC)
e.g. The inverse matrix of

$$\begin{pmatrix} 4 & 11 \\ 2 & 6 \end{pmatrix} \text{ is } \frac{1}{2}\begin{pmatrix} 6 & -11 \\ -2 & 4 \end{pmatrix} = \begin{pmatrix} 3 & -5\frac{1}{2} \\ -1 & 2 \end{pmatrix}$$

ISOSCELES TRAPEZIUM A trapezium which folds exactly on to itself. It has two pairs of equal angles and one pair of equal sides

e.g.

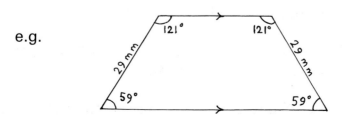

ISOSCELES TRIANGLE A triangle with two sides equal and two angles equal. Remember that the angle <u>between</u> the two equal sides is NOT one of the equal angles

e.g.

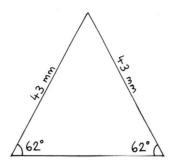

JOIN Connect together with a straight line

KITE A 4-sided plane figure with two pairs of equal sides, but no parallel sides. The diagonals of a kite cross at right angles

e.g.

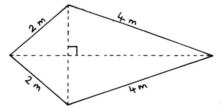

LABEL When you label something you put the correct letter or name on it

L.C.M. Lowest Common Multiple. The lowest number which two (or more) other numbers will divide into

e.g. The L.C.M. of 4, 5 and 6 is 60, because 60 is the lowest number that 4, 5 and 6 will all go into

The L.C.M. of 3, 6 and 24 is 24, because 24 is the lowest number that 3, 6 and 24 will all go into

LINE GRAPH A statistical diagram using a line
   e.g.

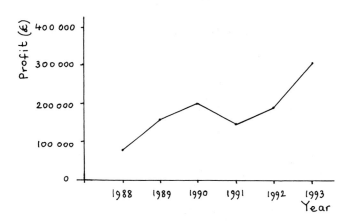

Profit of
Sunnyside
Products Ltd.
during the years
1988-93

LOCUS The path of a moving point

LOG (or LOGARITHM) A number expressed as a power of 10

   e.g. $100 = 10^2$ so the log of $100 = 2$
      $1000 = 10^3$ so   log $1000 = 3$,   etc.

   Log tables can be used for easy x and ÷ of difficult numbers

LOWEST TERMS A fraction is in its lowest terms when it is
   cancelled down as far as it will go

   e.g. $\frac{8}{20}$ is not in its lowest terms because it can be
   cancelled by 4

      $\frac{2}{5}$ is in its lowest terms because it cannot be
   cancelled any further

MAP When a figure maps on to something, it fits on to it exactly

MATRIX An arrangement of numbers in rows or columns surrounded by a bracket

e.g.
$$\begin{pmatrix} 3 & 4 & 15 & 0 \\ -4 & 3 & 1 & 8 \\ 7 & 0 & -1 & 5 \end{pmatrix}$$

MEAN Same thing as AVERAGE

$$\text{Mean} = \frac{\text{Sum of quantities}}{\text{Number of quantities}}$$

MEDIAN The middle number of a set of numbers placed in order of size

e.g.   32   35   36   36   38   39   42   45   47   51   51

The MEDIAN is 39

If there are two middle numbers, the median is the average of the two

MEDIATOR Same thing as PERPENDICULAR BISECTOR. A line which cuts another line exactly in half at right angles

e.g.

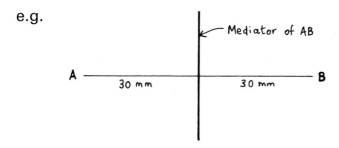

MINUS TIMES MINUS

Minus x Minus = Plus

e.g. $-2 \times -3 = +6$ $\qquad -3(-8) = +24$

$6 - (-5) = 6 + 5 = 11$

A minus number DIVIDED by a minus number also gives a plus number

e.g. $(-15) \div (-3) = +5$ $\qquad \dfrac{-28}{-7} = +4$

MIXED NUMBER A mixture of a whole number and a vulgar fraction

e.g.

$$2\tfrac{2}{3}, \quad 5\tfrac{1}{4}, \quad 1\tfrac{5}{16}$$

MODE In a set of numbers, the MODE is the number which occurs most often

e.g. In this set of numbers the mode is 27

24   27   26   28   28   27   29   32   27

MONEY

a) There are always TWO columns for the pence

e.g. Three pounds seven pence is £3.07
Three pounds seventy pence is £3.70

b) Amounts of £1 and over are written in pounds
Amounts of under £1 are written in either pounds or pence (but NOT BOTH)

e.g. Eighty–two pence is written £0.82 or 82p (but NOT £0.82p)

c) Pence is pronounced 'pence' (NOT 'pee')

MONTHS   Thirty days hath September,
         April, June and November.
      All the rest have thirty-one
         Excepting February alone
      Which hath but twenty-eight days clear
         And twenty-nine in each leap year.

      Remember FEB<u>R</u>UA<u>R</u>Y has two R's

MULTIPLE A number you get when you multiply things
    e.g. 15, 40, 65 and 95 are all multiples of 5 because they
    can all be obtained by multiplying by 5

NATURAL NUMBER A positive integer. A + whole number

NEGATIVE Less than nought. A negative number is a minus
    number

NEGATIVE ROTATION Same thing as CLOCKWISE rotation

NET The shape which a solid makes when its faces are spread
    out flat. The shape you would use to build a solid from a
    flat piece of card

    e.g. Net of a CUBE   Net of a SQUARE PYRAMID

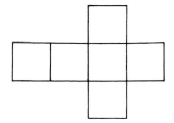 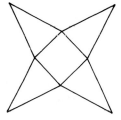

NONAGON A plane figure with 9 sides

NUMERATOR The top number of a fraction. The numerator
    tells you HOW MANY

OBTUSE ANGLE An angle of more than 90° but less than 180°

e.g.

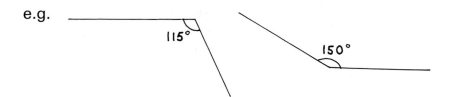

OCTAGON A plane figure with 8 sides

OCTAHEDRON A solid with 8 faces

OCTAL Counting in base 8

ORIGIN The point (0, 0) where the x axis crosses the y axis

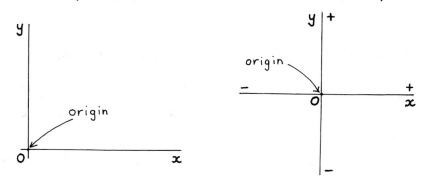

PARALLEL Parallel lines are lines which are always the same distance apart. They are marked with the same kind of arrows to show that they are parallel

e.g.

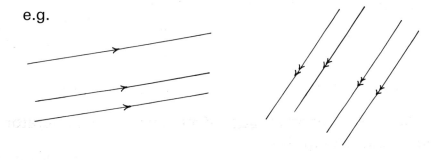

PARALLELOGRAM A 4–sided plane figure with two pairs of parallel sides

e.g.

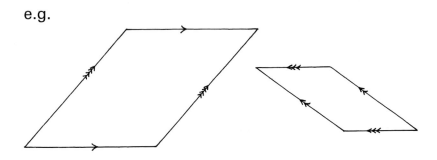

PENTAGON A plane figure with 5 sides

PER CENT Per cent, written %, means 'out of 100'
   <u>Per cent of</u>   can be written $\frac{\ \ }{100}$ x

e.g. <u>6 per cent of 35</u> can be written $\frac{6}{100}$ x $\frac{35}{1}$

To convert a fraction or a decimal to a percentage, multiply it by 100

e.g. $\frac{3}{4}$ as a percentage = $\frac{3}{4}$ x $\frac{100}{1}$ = **75%**

0.59 as a percentage = 0.59 x 100 = **59%**

PERIMETER The complete distance round the outside of a figure
   e.g. The perimeter of this rectangle is

5 + 2 + 5 + 2
= 14 cm

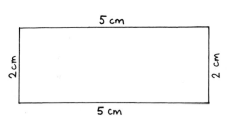

PERPENDICULAR At right angles

e.g. MN is perpendicular to AB

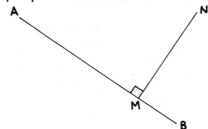

PERPENDICULAR BISECTOR A line which cuts another line exactly in half at right angles

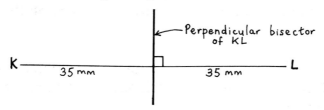

PI (π) Stands for 3.14 or $\frac{22}{7}$ (roughly). The distance ROUND a circle compared with the distance across it
e.g. If the distance across this circle is 10 m the distance ROUND it is

$$3.14 \times 10 = 31.4 \text{ m}$$

PICTOGRAM A statistical diagram made up of pictures
e.g.

BBC	𝚡 𝚡 𝚡 𝚡 𝚡 𝚡	Pictogram to show number of people in a certain town watching TV on a certain evening
ITV	𝚡 𝚡 𝚡 𝚡 𝚡 𝚡 𝟧	
Satellite	𝚡 𝚡 𝟧	(𝚡 represents 1000 people)

PIE CHART A statistical diagram shaped like a circular pie, with slices of pie showing the amounts

e.g.

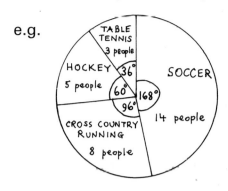

Pie chart to show how the 30 members of Form 3A spend a certain Games period

(Each person requires $\frac{360}{30} = 12°$)

When planning a pie chart, remember that all-the-way-round is 360°

PLANE FIGURE A flat figure. A figure which has length and width but no thickness, e.g. triangle, quadrilateral, hexagon, etc.

POLYGON A plane figure with many sides

Triangle - 3 sides
Quadrilateral - 4 sides
Pentagon - 5 sides
Hexagon - 6 sides
Heptagon - 7 sides
Octagon - 8 sides

Nonagon - 9 sides
Decagon - 10 sides
Hendecagon - 11 sides
Dodecagon - 12 sides
Quindecagon - 15 sides
Icosagon - 20 sides

POLYHEDRON A solid figure with many faces

Tetrahedron - 4 faces
Pentahedron - 5 faces
Hexahedron - 6 faces
Heptahedron - 7 faces

Octahedron - 8 faces
Decahedron - 10 faces
Dodecahedron - 12 faces
Icosahedron - 20 faces

POSITIVE More than nought. A positive number is a plus number

POSITIVE ROTATION Same thing as ANTICLOCKWISE rotation

POWER A small number placed next to an ordinary number to show how many times the ordinary number is multiplied by itself

e.g. 2^5 (called '2 to the power 5') means

$$2 \times 2 \times 2 \times 2 \times 2$$

PRE–MULTIPLY Multiply the right-hand matrix by the left-hand matrix

PRIME A prime number is a number which has only TWO factors (itself and 1). It is a number which will not divide by anything else but itself and 1

The LOWEST prime number is 2, and the first ten prime numbers are

2, 3, 5, 7, 11, 13, 17, 19, 23 and 29

PRISM A solid with both its ends exactly the same shape and size

e.g.

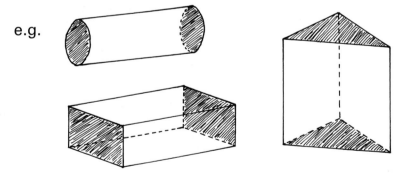

PROBABILITY The likelihood of something happening

e.g. (1) The probability that a coin will fall 'tails' up is one out of two (or $\frac{1}{2}$) because there are two possible ways it could fall

(2) The probability of a die falling with the ⚃ facing upwards is $\frac{1}{6}$ because there are 6 possible ways it could fall

RODUCE When you produce a line, you continue it further in the correct direction

e.g.

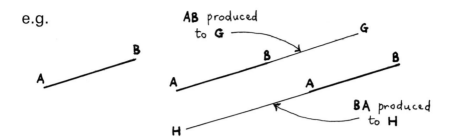

PRODUCT The answer to a multiplication

e.g. The product of 2 and 3 is 6 because 2 × 3 = 6

PYRAMID A solid with a special shape at one end (called the BASE) and a corner or point at the other end (called the APEX)

e.g.

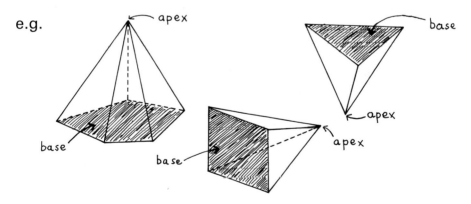

PYTHAGORAS' THEOREM In a right–angled triangle, the square of the hypotenuse is equal to the sum of the squares of the other two sides

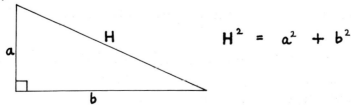

$$H^2 = a^2 + b^2$$

QUADRATIC EQUATION An equation with a SQUARED term in it

e.g. $x^2 + 2x - 15 = 0$

QUADRILATERAL (sometimes called QUAD) A plane figure with 4 sides

There are several special kinds of quadrilateral,

e.g. trapezium, parallelogram, rhombus, rectangle, square, kite, cyclic quad

QUOTIENT The answer to a division

RADIUS The distance from the centre of a circle to the circumference. Half the diameter

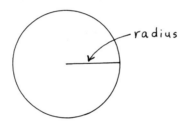

RATIO Numbers comparing the sizes of two (or more) quantities

Ratio is usually written with colons, e.g.

$$5 : 6 : 9$$

e.g. If John gets 50p spending money and Mike gets 75p, their spending money is in the ratio 50 : 75 which cancels down to 2 : 3

Always <u>cancel</u> ratios down as far as they will go

Ratios are always made up of WHOLE NUMBERS (not fractions)

RATIONAL NUMBER A number which can be obtained by dividing one quantity by another quantity. This includes all whole numbers and most fractions

RECIPROCAL (pronounced riss–ip–ro–kl) The 'other way up' of a fraction

e.g. The reciprocal of $\frac{7}{8}$ is $\frac{8}{7}$

The reciprocal of 6 is $\frac{1}{6}$

The reciprocal of $\frac{13}{4}$ is $\frac{4}{13}$

When a number is multiplied by its reciprocal, the answer is 1

RECTANGLE A 4–sided plane figure with right angles at all its corners

e.g.

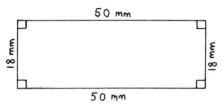

RECURRING DECIMAL A decimal which goes on the same way for ever

e.g. 32.666666666 written   32.66rec or 32.$\dot{6}$

5.81818181   written   5.8181rec or 5.$\dot{8}\dot{1}$

REFLECTION Reflecting a figure in a straight line (called a MIRROR LINE)

e.g.

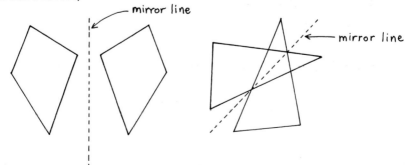

REFLEX ANGLE An angle of more than 180° but less than 360°
e.g.

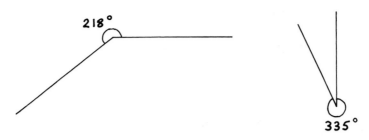

REGULAR A figure is called REGULAR when all its sides are
the same length and all its angles are the same size
e.g.

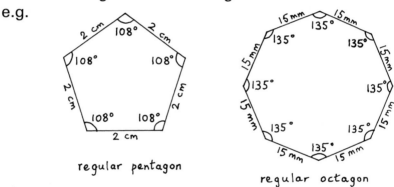

regular pentagon

regular octagon

RELATIONSHIP The way in which two or more things are
connected or related to each other

REVOLUTION All the way round. 360°

RHOMBUS A 4–sided plane figure with all its sides equal
e.g.

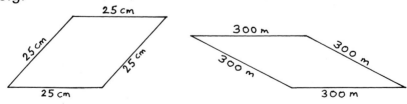

RIGHT ANGLE An angle of exactly 90°, usually shown like this

ROMAN NUMBERS

Most common ones used nowadays are

I = 1	L = 50	M = 1000
V = 5	C = 100	
X = 10	D = 500	

e.g. MDCCLXVIII   = 1000 + 500 + 200 + 50 + 10 + 5 + 3
                         = 1768

<u>Remember</u>

IV	=	4	(1 before 5)
IX	=	9	(1 before 10)
XL	=	40	(10 before 50)
XC	=	90	(10 before 100)
CM	=	900	(100 before 1000)

ROOT The number that a square or cube (or 'to the power') comes from

e.g. 5 squared (5 x 5) = 25
so the SQUARE ROOT of 25, written $\sqrt{25}$ = 5

4 cubed (4 x 4 x 4) = 64
so the CUBE ROOT of 64, written $\sqrt[3]{64}$ = 4

ROTATION Turning a figure about a point (called the centre of rotation)

e.g.

centre
of rotation

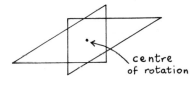
centre
of rotation

ROTATIONAL SYMMETRY A figure has rotational symmetry when you can turn it round and fit it exactly on to itself

If it fits 2 different ways, it has ROTATIONAL SYMMETRY of ORDER 2

If it fits 3 different ways, it has ROTATIONAL SYMMETRY of ORDER 3, etc.

e.g.

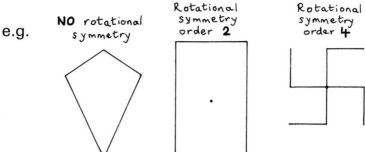

ROW MATRIX A matrix with only one row

e.g. $$\begin{pmatrix} 8 & 0 & -3 & 11 \end{pmatrix}$$

SCALENE TRIANGLE A triangle with no sides equal and no angles equal

SECTOR The part of a circle between two radii and an arc. A slice of a circular pie

e.g.

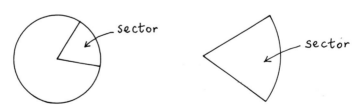

SEGMENT The part of a circle between a chord and an arc

e.g.

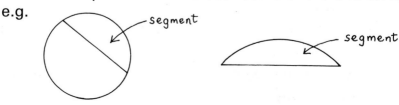

SEMICIRCLE Half a circle

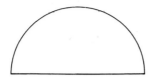

SET SIGNS

∈	is a member of	ℰ	universal set
∉	is not a member of	ø or { }	empty set
{ }	the set of	n(A)	number of elements in set A
⊂	is a subset of		
∩	intersection (cap)	A′	not A
∪	union (cup)		

SIGNIFICANT FIGURES The number of digits, not counting

noughts at the beginning

e.g.　　56.7　　　　　　has 3 significant figures

　　62554　　　　　　has 5 significant figures

　　　0.00093　　　　has 2 significant figures

SIGNS

=	is equal to
≏	is roughly equal to
<	is less than
>	is more than (or greater than)
≤	is less than or equal to
≥	is more than or equal to (is at least)
≠	is not equal to

$4 < N < 6\frac{1}{2}$　N is between 4 and $6\frac{1}{2}$ (N is more than 4 but less than $6\frac{1}{2}$)

≡	is congruent to
√	square root

SIMILAR Two or more figures (often triangles) which are
exactly the same shape – but they need not be the same
size and they need not be the same way round

e.g. All these triangles are similar

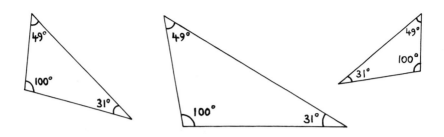

SIMPLIFY Work out to give the shortest possible answer

SIMULTANEOUS EQUATIONS Two (or more) equations
happening at the same time, with two (or more) different
letters to solve
e.g. $2a - b = 5$
$3a + 2b = 18$ which give the answer
$$\begin{cases} a = 4 \\ b = 3 \end{cases}$$

SINE of an angle (often written **sin**)

$$\text{Sine} = \frac{\text{Opposite}}{\text{Hypotenuse}}$$

e.g.

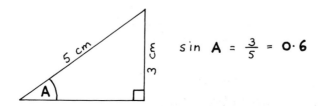

$\sin A = \frac{3}{5} = 0 \cdot 6$

SOLID A 3–dimensional figure. A figure which takes up space. A figure which has length, width and thickness, e.g. prism, pyramid, etc.

SOLVE Find the value of the letter

e.g. $4N + 2 = 26$

$N = 6$

SPEED

$$Speed = \frac{Distance}{Time}$$

If distance is in metres and time is in seconds, SPEED is in metres per second (or m/sec), etc.

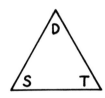

$S = \dfrac{D}{T}$, $T = \dfrac{D}{S}$, $D = ST$

$$Average\ speed = \frac{Total\ distance}{Total\ time}$$

SQUARE (1) A 4–sided plane figure with all its sides equal and right angles at its corners

e.g.

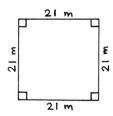

(2)   A number multiplied by itself
e.g. The square of $5 = 5 \times 5 = 25$

<u>Squared</u> means 'multiplied by itself'
It is written to the power 2
e.g.   6 squared $= 6^2 = 6 \times 6 = 36$

SQUARE ROOT The number that a square has come from

    e.g. 25 is the square of 5 , so 5 is the SQUARE ROOT of 25

         64 is the square of 8 , so 8 is the SQUARE ROOT of 64

  Square root is written $\sqrt{}$ or $\sqrt{\;}$, e.g. $\sqrt{64} = 8$

STANDARD FORM A short way of writing very large or very small numbers

    e.g. 970000000000   in standard form is 9.7×10^{11}

          5000000   in standard form is 5×10^{6}

     0.0000000834   in standard form is 8.34×10^{-8}

STATISTICAL DIAGRAM A way of showing amounts by drawing a picture. The best-known statistical diagrams are Bar Charts, Block Graphs, Column Graphs, Pictograms, Histograms, Pie Charts and Line Graphs

SUBSET A set which fits inside another set

  e.g. 'brown bears' is a subset of 'bears' because all brown bears are bears

  'prime numbers' is a subset of 'numbers' because all prime numbers are numbers

  Subset is written $\subset$

  e.g {brown bears} $\subset$ {bears}

       {prime numbers} $\subset$ {numbers}

SUM The answer to an addition

  e.g. The sum of 24, 15 and 37 is 76, because

             $24 + 15 + 37 = 76$

SUPPLEMENTARY ANGLES Angles which add up to 180°

e.g.

Angles A and B
are supplementary

SURFACE AREA The total surface area of a solid is all the areas of its faces added together. If in doubt, draw the NET of the solid

e.g. Total surface area of this cuboid is 202 cm²

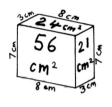

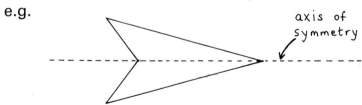

Total surface area
= 56 + 24 + 21
+ 56 + 24 + 21
= 202 cm²

SYMMETRY

Axis of symmetry A folding line which makes one half of a figure fit (or map) exactly on to the other half. The figure is SYMMETRICAL about the folding line

e.g.

axis of
symmetry

Rotational symmetry A figure has rotational symmetry when you can turn it round and fit it exactly on to itself. If it fits 2 different ways, it has rotational symmetry of ORDER 2

If it fits 3 different ways, it has rotational symmetry of ORDER 3, etc.

e.g.

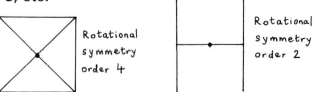

Rotational
symmetry
order 4

Rotational
symmetry
order 2

TANGENT (1) A straight line which just touches the circumference of a circle

e.g.

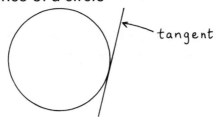

tangent

(2) Tangent of an angle (often written **tan**)

$$\text{Tangent} = \frac{\text{Opposite}}{\text{Adjacent}}$$

e.g.

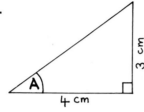

$\tan A = \frac{3}{4} = 0{\cdot}75$

TERM One of the parts of an expression

e.g.　$4a^2 + 5a - 8$　has 3 terms ($4a^2$, $5a$ and -8)

TESSELLATION A pattern of plane figures fitting together exactly (with no gaps between the figures)

e.g.　*hexagons*　　　　　　　　　　　　　*octagons and squares*

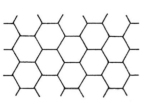
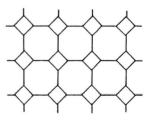

TETRAHEDRON A solid with 4 triangular faces. A triangular pyramid

e.g.

TRANSFORMATION When one figure is changed into another by reflection, rotation, translation, enlargement, etc.

TRANSLATION Moving the position of something so that it stays the same way up and the same way round

e.g.

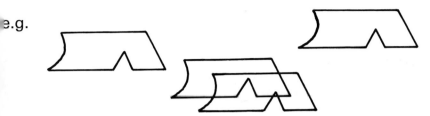

TRANSVERSAL A straight line which crosses other lines

e.g.

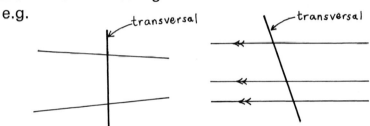

TRAPEZIUM A 4–sided figure with one pair of parallel sides

e.g.

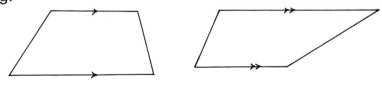

An ISOSCELES TRAPEZIUM also has 2 equal sides and 2 pairs of equal angles

e.g.

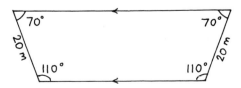

TRAVEL GRAPH A graph to show a journey or journeys
<u>Time</u> goes along the bottom (horizontal axis)
<u>Distance from a certain place</u> goes up the side
(vertical axis)

e.g.

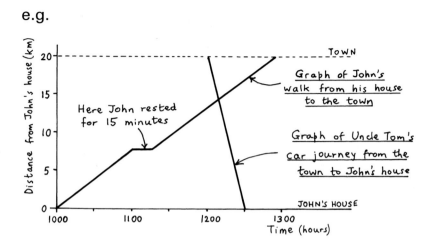

TRIANGLE A plane figure with 3 sides

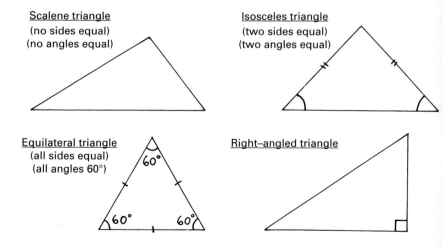

TRIGONOMETRY The part of maths that deals with measuring triangles (using sines, cosines and tangents, etc.)

TRINOMIAL An expression containing 3 terms
e.g. $2x^2 - 5x + 18$

UNIFORM Always the same. Not changing

UNION A set containing ALL the elements in both (or all) the original sets, but not repeating any of them. Union is written ∪

e.g.   The UNION of these two sets
Set A = {2, 3, 5, 7, 11, 13}
Set B = {2, 4, 6, 8, 10}

is   {2, 3, 4, 5, 6, 7, 8, 10, 11, 13}

which is called A ∪ B

UNIVERSAL SET The big set which contains all the things you are dealing with. Everything in every set must be in the universal set

Universal set is written Ɛ

VALUE The amount (in numbers) which you get as the answer
e.g. (1)   If a=2, b=3, the value of a+a+b is 7
because 2 + 2 + 3 = 7

(2)   The value of 4^3 is 64
because 4 x 4 x 4 = 64

VECTOR The movement of a point a certain distance in a certain direction

e.g.

Vector $\overrightarrow{AB}$ = $\begin{pmatrix} 3 \\ 2 \end{pmatrix}$

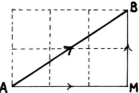

AM (3 units) and MB (2 units) are the COMPONENTS and AB is their RESULTANT

The arrow on the resultant always goes round the triangle in the opposite direction to the arrows on the components

VENN DIAGRAM A picture showing sets. The elements (or members) of each set are put in a circle or oval or sausage shape

e.g. The set F contains the numbers 5, 10, 15, 20

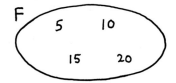

The set G contains the numbers 5, 6, 7, 8, 9, 10, 11

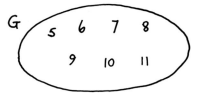

The set H contains the numbers 5, 15

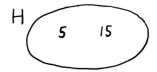

The set J contains the numbers 31, 32, 33

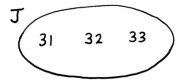

These sets can be combined in three different ways
(1) Two DISJOINT sets (nothing in common)

e.g.

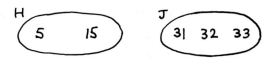

(2) One set as a SUBSET of another (one set fits inside another)

e.g.

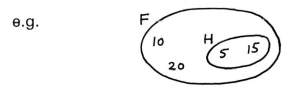

(3) Sets with an INTERSECTION (they have some things in common)

e.g.

UNIVERSAL SET is usually drawn as a rectangle which everything else fits into

Some useful Venn diagram patterns

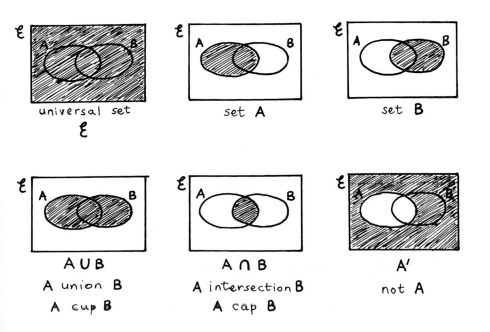

VERTEX A corner. Several corners are called VERTICES (pronounced verti–seez)

e.g. A triangle has 3 vertices

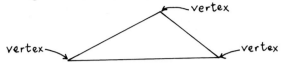

A square (Egyptian) pyramid has 5 vertices

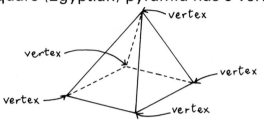

VERTICAL Straight up and down. At right angles to horizontal

VERTICALLY OPPOSITE ANGLES Angles on the opposite sides of an X shape
Vertically opposite angles are EQUAL

e.g.

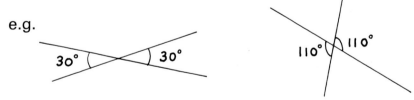

VOLUME The amount of space inside a solid.
Volume is always measured in CUBIC units (e.g. cubic metres, cubic centimetres, litres, etc.)

Remember 1000 CUBIC CENTIMETRES = 1 LITRE

Volume of cuboid = length x width x height
e.g. The volume of this cuboid is
8 x 3 x 4 = 96 cm³ (96 cubic centimetres)

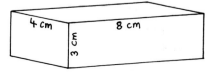

<u>Volume of prism</u> = area of base x height
     e.g. The volume of this prism is
     12 x 13 = 156 m³ (156 cubic metres)

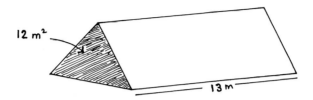

VOLUMES OF SIMILAR FIGURES

If length is 2 times, VOLUME is 8 times   (2 x 2 x 2)
If length is 3 times, VOLUME is 27 times   (3 x 3 x 3)
If length is 4 times, VOLUME is 64 times   (4 x 4 x 4)

                                             etc.

VULGAR FRACTION An ordinary fraction with one number
over the other

e.g. $\dfrac{3}{5}$, $\dfrac{1}{16}$, $\dfrac{7}{8}$

X AXIS, Y AXIS

X axis is the horizontal (ALONG) axis
Y axis is the vertical (UP) axis

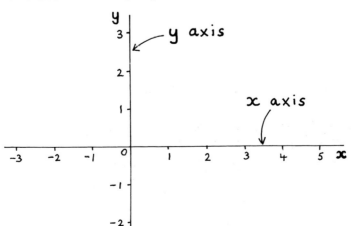

MULTIPLICATION TABLES 2x, 3x, 4x, 5x

1	x	2	=	2		1	x	3	=	3
2	x	2	=	4		2	x	3	=	6
3	x	2	=	6		3	x	3	=	9
4	x	2	=	8		4	x	3	=	12
5	x	2	=	10		5	x	3	=	15
6	x	2	=	12		6	x	3	=	18
7	x	2	=	14		7	x	3	=	21
8	x	2	=	16		8	x	3	=	24
9	x	2	=	18		9	x	3	=	27
10	x	2	=	20		10	x	3	=	30
11	x	2	=	22		11	x	3	=	33
12	x	2	=	24		12	x	3	=	36

1	x	4	=	4		1	x	5	=	5
2	x	4	=	8		2	x	5	=	10
3	x	4	=	12		3	x	5	=	15
4	x	4	=	16		4	x	5	=	20
5	x	4	=	20		5	x	5	=	25
6	x	4	=	24		6	x	5	=	30
7	x	4	=	28		7	x	5	=	35
8	x	4	=	32		8	x	5	=	40
9	x	4	=	36		9	x	5	=	45
10	x	4	=	40		10	x	5	=	50
11	x	4	=	44		11	x	5	=	55
12	x	4	=	48		12	x	5	=	60

MULTIPLICATION TABLES 6x, 7x, 8x, 9x

1	x	6	=	6		1	x	7	=	7
2	x	6	=	12		2	x	7	=	14
3	x	6	=	18		3	x	7	=	21
4	x	6	=	24		4	x	7	=	28
5	x	6	=	30		5	x	7	=	35
6	x	6	=	36		6	x	7	=	42
7	x	6	=	42		7	x	7	=	49
8	x	6	=	48		8	x	7	=	56
9	x	6	=	54		9	x	7	=	63
10	x	6	=	60		10	x	7	=	70
11	x	6	=	66		11	x	7	=	77
12	x	6	=	72		12	x	7	=	84

1	x	8	=	8		1	x	9	=	9
2	x	8	=	16		2	x	9	=	18
3	x	8	=	24		3	x	9	=	27
4	x	8	=	32		4	x	9	=	36
5	x	8	=	40		5	x	9	=	45
6	x	8	=	48		6	x	9	=	54
7	x	8	=	56		7	x	9	=	63
8	x	8	=	64		8	x	9	=	72
9	x	8	=	72		9	x	9	=	81
10	x	8	=	80		10	x	9	=	90
11	x	8	=	88		11	x	9	=	99
12	x	8	=	96		12	x	9	=	108

MULTIPLICATION TABLES 10x, 11x, 12x, 13x

1	x	10	=	10	1	x	11	=	11
2	x	10	=	20	2	x	11	=	22
3	x	10	=	30	3	x	11	=	33
4	x	10	=	40	4	x	11	=	44
5	x	10	=	50	5	x	11	=	55
6	x	10	=	60	6	x	11	=	66
7	x	10	=	70	7	x	11	=	77
8	x	10	=	80	8	x	11	=	88
9	x	10	=	90	9	x	11	=	99
10	x	10	=	100	10	x	11	=	110
11	x	10	=	110	11	x	11	=	121
12	x	10	=	120	12	x	11	=	132

1	x	12	=	12	1	x	13	=	13
2	x	12	=	24	2	x	13	=	26
3	x	12	=	36	3	x	13	=	39
4	x	12	=	48	4	x	13	=	52
5	x	12	=	60	5	x	13	=	65
6	x	12	=	72	6	x	13	=	78
7	x	12	=	84	7	x	13	=	91
8	x	12	=	96	8	x	13	=	104
9	x	12	=	108	9	x	13	=	117
10	x	12	=	120	10	x	13	=	130
11	x	12	=	132	11	x	13	=	143
12	x	12	=	144	12	x	13	=	156

SQUARES AND CUBES

	Square	Cube		Square	Cube
1	1	1	**11**	121	1331
2	4	8	**12**	144	1728
3	9	27	**13**	169	2197
4	16	64	**14**	196	2744
5	25	125	**15**	225	3375
6	36	216	**16**	256	4096
7	49	343	**17**	289	4913
8	64	512	**18**	324	5832
9	81	729	**19**	361	6859
10	100	1000	**20**	400	8000

SOME USEFUL FRACTIONS, DECIMALS AND PERCENTAGES

$\frac{1}{2}$ = 0.5 = 50%

$\frac{1}{4}$ = 0.25 = 25%

$\frac{3}{4}$ = 0.75 = 75%

$\frac{1}{5}$ = 0.2 = 20%

$\frac{1}{10}$ = 0.1 = 10%

$\frac{1}{100}$ = 0.01 = 1%

$\frac{1}{8}$ = 0.125 = $12\frac{1}{2}$%

$\frac{1}{3}$ = 0.33 rec = $33\frac{1}{3}$%

$\frac{2}{3}$ = 0.66 rec = $66\frac{2}{3}$%

METRIC MEASUREMENT

LENGTH

10 millimetres	= 1 centimetre	10 mm	= 1 cm
100 centimetres	= 1 metre	100 cm	= 1 m
1000 millimetres	= 1 metre	1000 mm	= 1 m
1000 metres	= 1 kilometre	1000 m	= 1 km

MASS

1000 milligrams	= 1 gram	1000 mg	= 1 g
1000 grams	= 1 kilogram (1 kilo)	1000 g	= 1 kg
1000 kilograms	= 1 tonne	1000 kg	= 1 t

AREA

100 square metres	= 1 are	$100m^2$	= 1 a
100 ares	= 1 hectare	100 a	= 1 ha

VOLUME

1000 cubic centimetres	= 1 litre	$1000 cm^3$	= 1 l
1 cubic centimetre	= 1 millilitre	$1 cm^3$	= 1 ml

MONEY

100 pence	= 1 pound	100p	= £1
100 cents	= 1 euro	100c	= €1

METRIC COLUMNS

kilo–	hecto–	deca–	*	deci–	centi–	milli–
k–	h–	da–		d–	c–	m–

e.g. Length

km	hm	dam	m	dm	cm	mm
(King	Henry's	daughter	Mary	drinks	cows'	milk)

kilo–	1000	times
hecto–	100	times
deca–	10	times
deci–	$\frac{1}{10}$	of
centi–	$\frac{1}{100}$	of
milli–	$\frac{1}{1000}$	of

Do not put the letter 's' after units, e.g.
345cm (NOT 345 cms)

TIME

60 seconds	=	1 minute
60 minutes	=	1 hour
24 hours	=	1 day
7 days	=	1 week
12 months	=	1 year
365 days	=	1 year
366 days	=	1 leap year
10 years	=	1 decade
100 years	=	1 century

NON-METRIC MEASUREMENT

Figures on the right-hand side are the rough equivalents (same amounts) in metric units, correct to 3 significant figures)

LENGTH

12 inches	= 1 foot	=	30.5cm
3 feet	= 1 yard...	=	91.4cm
1760 yards	= 1 mile	=	1.61km
8 furlongs	= 1 mile	=	1.61km
	(racetracks)		
4 inches	= 1 hand (1 hh)	=	10.2cm
	(horses' heights)		
6 feet	= 1 fathom	=	1.83m
	(depths of water)		

MASS

16 ounces	= 1 pound (16 oz = 1 lb)	=	454g
14 pounds	= 1 stone	=	6.35kg
2240 pounds	= 1 ton..	=	1.02t

AREA

4840 square yards = 1 acre	=	0.405ha

VOLUME

8 pints	= 1 gallon....................................	=	4.55*l*

SPEED

1 knot	= 1 nautical mile/hour	=	1.85km/h
	(or 1.15 miles/hour)		

SOME USEFUL GRAPHS

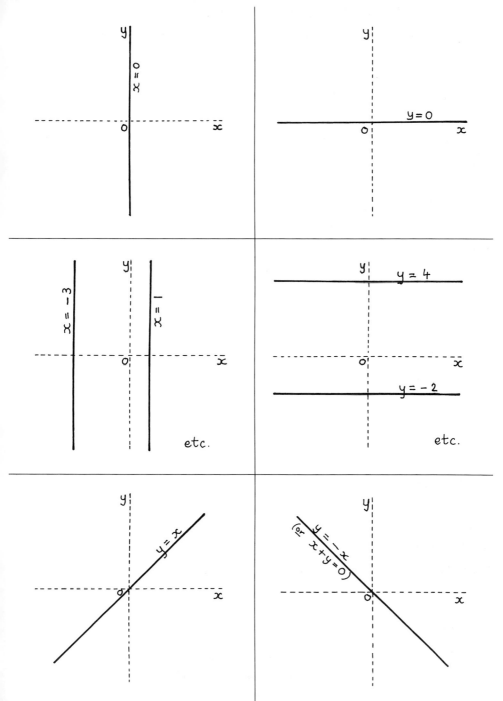

SOME CIRCLE RULES

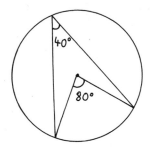

Angle at the centre
is twice the angle
at the circumference

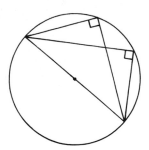

Angles in a
semicircle
are right angles

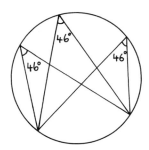

Angles in the
same segment
are equal

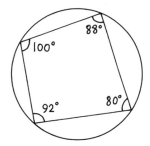

Opposite angles
of a cyclic quad
add up to 180°

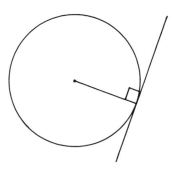

Tangent is at
right angles
to radius